NOTE TO PARENTS

The four stories in this book are adaptations of
parables that Jesus told. Each one is delightfully
illustrated and carefully retold in modern English.
The special message contained in each story is
clearly explained for children.

The Stories Jesus Told

retold by Marjorie Newman
illustrated by Dianne Stuchbury

Copyright © 1990 World International Publishing Limited.
All rights reserved.
Published in Great Britain by World International Publishing Limited,
An Egmont Company, Egmont House,
P.O. Box 111, Great Ducie Street,
Manchester M60 3BL.
Printed in DDR.
ISBN 0 7235 4471 9

A CIP catalogue record for this book is available from the British Library

THE LOST SHEEP

Once there was a shepherd who had a hundred
sheep. He knew each one by name. And he
loved them.

Every day, he led his sheep over the hills until
he found fresh grass for them to eat, and cool
water for them to drink.

Every night the shepherd led the sheep safely back to the fold. As they went in, he counted them. One, two, three, four... right up to ninety-seven, ninety-eight, ninety-nine, one hundred!

But one night, he counted ninety-seven...
ninety-eight... ninety-nine... And that was all!
One sheep was lost. It must be out on the
hillside, alone, he thought.

The shepherd was tired. He was cold and hungry. But he didn't think about himself. He left the ninety-nine sheep safely in the fold, and set out in the darkness to find the one which was lost.

Alone on the hillside, a frightened sheep called
'Baa! Baa!' It had fallen into a hole, and couldn't
get out.

The shepherd kept on searching...

And at last the shepherd found the sheep!
He was very, very glad. Tenderly he rescued it.
Then he carried it home on his shoulders.
singing all the way.

Jesus said, "God, your Heavenly Father, is like this shepherd. He loves you and takes care of you, just as the shepherd cares for his sheep. And He will never leave you to be sad and alone."

THE VISITOR AT MIDNIGHT

The children had been playing outside. They were hungry for their supper! They ate up every scrap of the bread Mum had made. "Never mind," smiled Mum. "I'll bake some more in the morning."

But that night, there was a loud knocking on the door of their house. Dad opened the door. "It's our friend from far away!" he cried. "He's very tired and hungry."

"I'll get a meal ready!" said Mum.

Mum scrambled out of bed. Then she remembered! They had no bread left! She whispered to Dad.   Dad nodded.

Quickly, Dad ran down the street to their neighbour's house. He banged on the door. Presently, a sleepy voice called, "Who's there? Go away! We're all in bed!"

But Dad *had* to have the bread. He kept on knocking.

At last, grumbling, the neighbour came to the door. He gave Dad some bread. Dad ran home. And the family had a midnight feast!

Jesus said, "When you pray, don't give up too soon! If a grumpy neighbour will get up at midnight to give bread to a friend, you can be sure God will give *you* what is good for you, if you keep on asking!"

THE MUSTARD SEED

One day a man found a mustard seed. "I've never seen such a small seed!" he said. "It's the smallest seed there is! I shall plant it in my field, to see if it will grow." So he did.

The rain rained. The sun shone. The wind blew. The man kept looking to see if the mustard seed was sprouting yet. "I expect it will grow into a very small tree," he said.

But the mustard seed grew and grew! It grew into a huge tree. The tree was so big, birds came and nested in its branches. What a surprise!

Jesus said, "Small things are important! And God can make great things grow from small beginnings!"

THE HOUSE ON THE ROCK

Once there were two men. Each man wanted to build a house for himself. The first man searched for a good place for a house. There he dug deep into the ground until he came to firm rock. Then he started to build.

The second man didn't bother *where* his house went. He didn't bother to dig deep. He built his house on sand.

Presently, the houses were finished. They both looked fine – until a storm began to blow. The wind howled. The rain lashed down. Flood waters rose. The storm beat upon the houses.

The house built on rock stood firm. But –

– the house on the sand fell FLAT!

Jesus said, "If you try to live as I show you, you are like the first man. When troubles come, you will not give in. But if you take no notice of my words, you are like the second man. When troubles come, you will not be able to manage."